WORSHIP **SONGBOOK**

©2000 Integrity Incorporated
1000 Cody Road, Mobile, AL 36695-3425
All Songs Used By Permission. All Rights Reserved.
International Rights Secured.

Above All

**Words and Music by
LENNY LeBLANC and
PAUL BALOCHE**

As the Deer

Words and Music by
MARTIN J. NYSTROM

heart's de - sire,___ and I___ long to___ wor - ship Thee.

You a - lone are my strength, my shield; to You a - lone may my

spir - it yield. You a - lone are my heart's de - sire,___ and I

long to wor - ship Thee. Thee.

Awesome God

Words and Music by
RICH MULLINS

Better Is One Day

Words and Music by
MATT REDMAN

Celebrate Jesus

**Words and Music by
GARY OLIVER**

Cel - e - brate Je - sus, cel - e - brate.

Cel - e - brate Je - sus, cel - e - brate.

Cel - e - brate Je - sus, cel - e - brate.

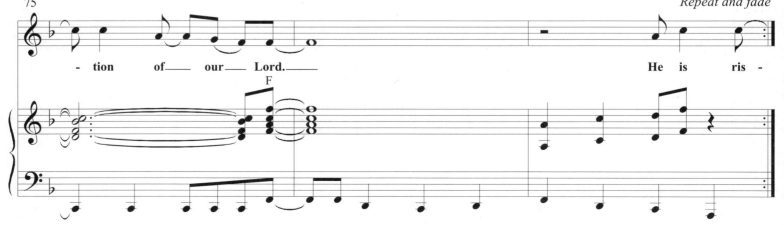

Did You Feel the Mountains Tremble?

Words and Music by
MARTIN SMITH

Acoustic rock ♩ = 102

1. Did you feel the moun-tains trem-ble?___ Did you hear___ the
2. Did you feel the peo-ple trem-ble?___ Did you hear___ the
3. Do you feel the dark-ness trem-ble___ when all the saints___ join

o-ceans roar when the peo-ple rose to sing of___
sing-ers roar when the lost be-gan to sing of___
in one song? And all the streams flow as one riv-er___

2nd time to Coda

Your joy,___ danc - ers___ who dance___ up - on in - jus -

tice.___

Glorify Thy Name

Words and Music by
DONNA ADKINS

God Is Good All the Time

Words and Music by
DON MOEN and
PAUL OVERSTREET

God Will Make a Way

Words and Music by
DON MOEN

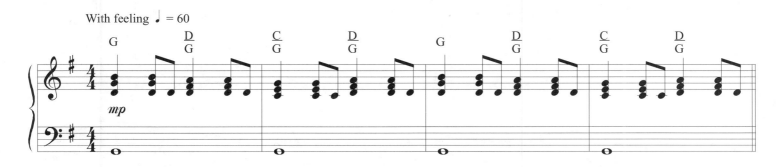

God will make a way where there seems to be no way. He

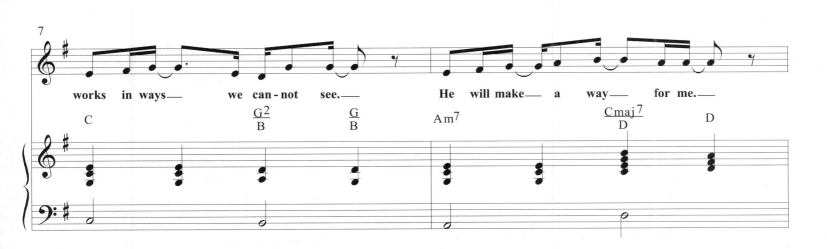

works in ways we can-not see. He will make a way for me.

He Is Able

**Words and Music by
RORY NOLAND and
GREG FERGUSON**

50

make me what He wants___ me___ to be.___

Holy and Anointed One

Words and Music by
JOHN BARNETT

Holy Ground

Words and Music by
GERON DAVIS

Hungry (Falling on My Knees)

Words and Music by
KATHRYN SCOTT

Moderately ♩ = 86

1. Hun - gry, I___ come to___ You, for___ I know___ You sat - is - fy.___
2. Bro - ken, I___ run to___ You, for___ Your arms___ are o - pen wide;___

I am emp - ty,___ but___ I know___ Your love___
I am wea - ry,___ but___ I know___ Your touch___

I Believe in Jesus

Words and Music by
MARC NELSON

1. I_____ be - lieve in__ Je - sus;____
2.3. I_____ be - lieve in__ You,_ Lord;____

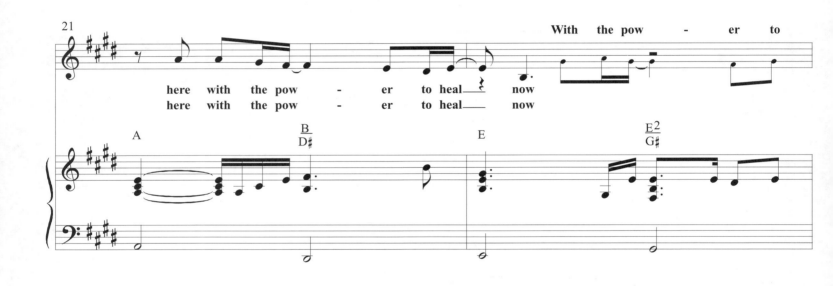

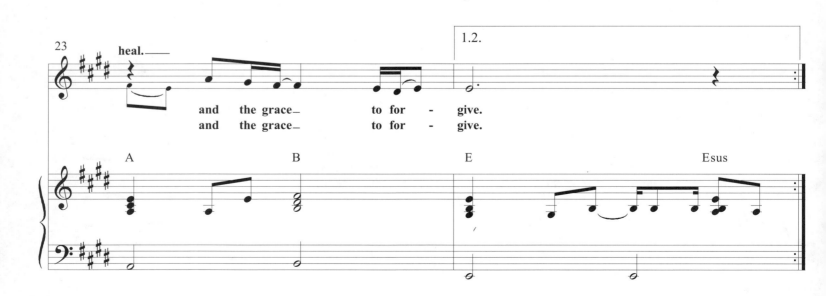

I See the Lord

Words and Music by
CHRIS FALSON

Worshipfully ♩ = 76-80
B F♯/A♯ C♯m7 B/D♯ Emaj7 F♯sus F♯/A♯
mp
5
B F♯/A♯ C♯m7 B/D♯ E6 E C♯m/F♯
3
9
I see the Lord seat - ed on the throne ex -
B F♯/A♯ C♯m7 B/D♯ E2
12
alt - ed, and the train of His robe fills the tem - ple with glo -
E/F♯ F♯ B F♯/A♯ C♯m7 B/D♯

I Walk by Faith

Words and Music by
CHRIS FALSON

I Will Celebrate

**Words and Music by
RITA BALOCHE**

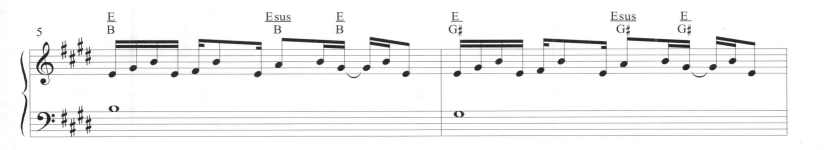

25

wor - ship - ping— Him.

E
B   F#m7
            B

CODA

27

wor - ship - ping— Him.

E
B   F#m7
            B

29

I—— will cel - e - brate,—— sing—— un - to the Lord,——

E   Esus   E   E   Esus   E
                          C#   C#   C#

31

sing—— to the Lord—— a new—— song.——

E   A   E   Esus   E
A   B

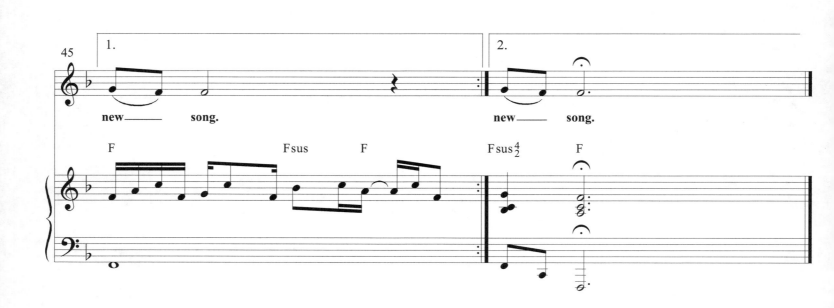

I Will Not Forget You

Words and Music by
BEN and ROBIN PASLEY

In That Day

Words and Music by
JOSEPH SABOLICK

Driving rock ♩ = 124

In the Secret

Words and Music by
ANDY PARK

this bar 1st time only

Jesus Is Alive

Words and Music by
RON KENOLY

Jesus, Lover of My Soul

Words and Music by
JOHN EZZY, DANIEL GRUL, and
STEPHEN McPHERSON

Light the Fire Again

**Words and Music by
BRAIN DOERKSEN**

CODA

opt. SOLO ad lib fills

a - gain.

1.2.3.

4.

Lord, light the fire—   Lord, light the fire— a - gain.

Redeemer, Savior, Friend

Words and Music by
DARRELL EVANS and
CHRIS SPRINGER

Rock of Ages

Words and Music by
RITA BALOCHE

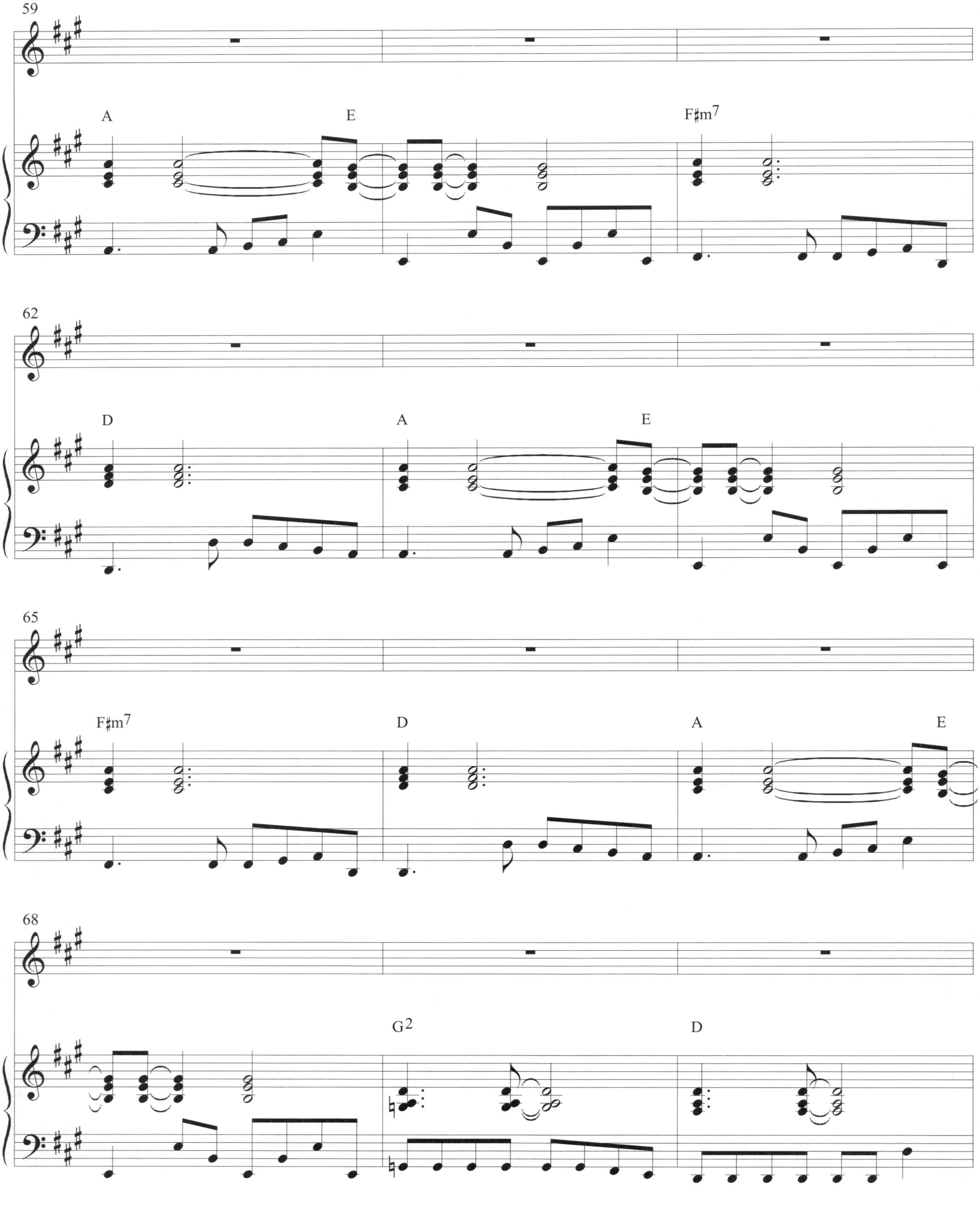
59
A
E
F♯m7
62
D
A
E
65
F♯m7
D
A
E
68
G2
D

Shine, Jesus, Shine

**Words and Music by
GRAHAM KENDRICK**

With excitement ♩ = 126

Shine, Je - sus, shine,—— fill this land with the Fa - ther's glo - ry. Blaze, Spir - it, blaze,—— set our hearts on fire.

There Is None Like You

Words and Music by
LENNY LeBLANC

Victory Chant

Words and Music by
JOSEPH VOGELS

We Want to See Jesus Lifted High

**Words and Music by
DOUG HORLEY**

150

We Will Dance

Words and Music by
DAVID RUIS

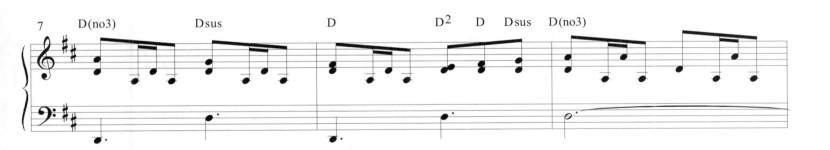

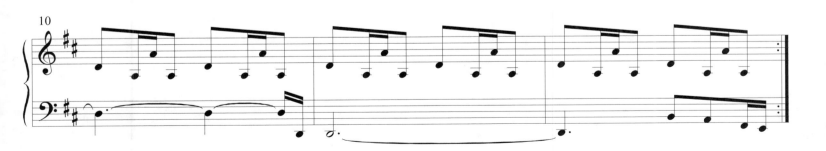

When I Look into Your Holiness

Words and Music by
WAYNE and CATHY PERRIN

Worship You

Words and Music by
JAMI SMITH

know-ing it's— the best that we— can— do.

do to fall on our face,— fall on our face,—

fall on our face— in front of— You.

(vocal 1st time only)

Repeat and fade

You Are God

Words and Music by
SCOTT UNDERWOOD

are,_____ You are God,_____ You are

God,_____ God,_____ God._____ You are.

Mmm_____ 3. You are

D.S. al CODA 𝄋